BRITAIN IN PICTURES
THE BRITISH PEOPLE IN PICTURES

BRITISH MAPS AND MAP-MAKERS

GENERAL EDITOR
W. J. TURNER

BRITISH
MAPS AND MAP-MAKERS

EDWARD LYNAM

WITH
8 PLATES IN COLOUR
AND
22 ILLUSTRATIONS IN
BLACK & WHITE

WILLIAM COLLINS OF LONDON
MCMXXXXIV

PRODUCED BY
ADPRINT LIMITED LONDON
——
SECOND IMPRESSION

PRINTED IN GREAT BRITAIN BY
CLARKE & SHERWELL LTD NORTHAMPTON
ON MELLOTEX BOOK PAPER MADE BY
TULLIS RUSSELL & CO LTD MARKINCH SCOTLAND

LIST OF ILLUSTRATIONS

PLATES IN COLOUR

BLACK AND WHITE ILLUSTRATIONS

A SHORT BIBLIOGRAPHY

W. L. Bevan and H. W. Phillot : *Mediæval
Geography : An Essay.* London, 1873.

Edward Lynam : *Introduction to Saxton's
Atlas of England and Wales*, 1574-1579.
British Museum, 1939.

Facsimile Reproductions of all the Maps in
Saxton's *Atlas*, 1574-1579. British Museum,
1933.

Thomas Chubb : *The Printed Maps in the
Atlases of Great Britain and Ireland : a
Bibliography*, 1579-1870. London, 1927.

Sir George Fordham : *Some Notable Surveyors & Map-Makers of the 16th, 17th
and 18th Centuries and their Work.* Cambridge, 1929.

John Norden : *Speculum Britanniae Pars.
Historical and Chorographical Description
of the County of Essex*, 1594. Edited by
Sir Henry Ellis. London, 1840.

Sir Charles Close : *The Early Years of the
Ordnance Survey.* London, 1926

Professor Frank Debenham : *Map Making.*
London, 1936.

ASTROLABE, C. 1450

ABBEYS, MANORS AND WAYFARERS
1250-1500

Map making is of very great antiquity, almost as ancient as the ownership of land or of organized movements by bodies of men. Before 2,000 B.C., rich Babylonians were having plans of their private estates moulded in clay, and by 300 B.C., the Greeks had mapped upon tablets most of the lands and seas of the Levant. Our Anglo-Saxon, Scandinavian and Norman forbears must have made many local maps, however crude, during the centuries when they were clearing, building, colonising and fighting all over England ; yet nothing by them has come down to us from before 1250, except a few small scholastic maps which were drawn in monasteries to illustrate Scriptural commentaries or late classical works on geography, and they had no relation to national topography.

Between 300 B.C. and 170 A.D. the Greeks, by observations of the sun, moon and stars from Assouan, Rhodes, Marseilles and other stations, had determined approximately the latitude and longitude, and therefore the size, of a large number of places in the world they knew, including Britain. The practical Romans neglected astronomy ; but some of their consuls and officials, such as Caesar and Pliny, wrote valuable descriptions of parts of the Empire, while the Emperors Augustus and Theodosius had maps made of the known world. Although these maps have disappeared, and others, such as the masterly atlas of the world by Ptolemy, were temporarily lost at the fall of the Western Empire in 476, the descriptions of Pliny, Mela and others survived in copies made by early Christian writers. In the monastic libraries of thirteenth century England there was therefore ample material for a rough map of the country.

7

As often happened in later times, the first really English cartographers were inspired by an historian. Before 1150 a school of annalists, which soon became famous, had been formed by the Benedictines at their Abbey of St. Albans, and in 1250, Matthew Paris, our greatest historian since Bede, was its director. From him and his pupils we have a notable map of England, the first since that of Claudius Ptolemy, c. 168 A.D, to represent England separately. To what he had gleaned from books Matthew added much from his own knowledge and from reports given him by merchants, sailors, soldiers and monks from other monasteries. Distances he would have known from his manuscript sources and from contemporary reckonings in miles ; but it is as well that he has given no scale to this map. Directions presented a more difficult problem, and probably the only objects then used for large surveys in England were sun-dials with various kinds of hour-glasses for observing the positions of the sun, and a compass which consisted merely of a needle, periodically magnetized with a lode-stone, riding in a piece of cork, which was placed in a bowl of water. The polar star hung approximately over the true North, and from it and the sun, latitude could be roughly calculated.

It seems, however, that Matthew's map was not intended to be wholly accurate. Its main object was to show English pilgrims—and perhaps also Crusaders and troops bound for France—their shortest route to Dover, the port of embarkation for the continental places of pilgrimage and for Normandy and Picardy. This purpose is clear from the many deliberate distortions in south, central and south-eastern England, such as placing Middlesex in the east Midlands, Suffolk at the south-east corner of the country, and the mouth of the Thames and Dover near the centre of the south coast. In fact, a large proportion of the country was delineated diagrammatically so that pilgrims and Crusaders might see at a glance all the towns, monasteries and monastic guest-houses along their route.

Nevertheless the map has much general interest. Here are many ports, such as Orford, Shoreham, and Wallsend, which have long fallen into disuse, river ports such as Boroughbridge (Pons Burgi) and North-allerton, and important river crossings like Earlsferry and Queensferry. The Yorkshire Moors are shown as Blakhamor, extending from Tyne to Humber ; Windsor Forest appears as a "vivarium" south of Windsor ; and the Peak in Derbyshire has its famous Cave of the Winds. Many of the legends on the map, such as that describing southern Wales as full of mountains, forests and marshes, and its people as uncultured, warlike and boastful of their descent from the Greeks, are copied from the Roman descriptions, while Scotland, about which the Romans knew little and the English of 1250 not much more, is depicted very inaccurately. In other ways Matthew reveals knowledge of the science of cartography. He has oriented this map to the north, although almost all contemporary foreign maps were oriented to the east, where lay both the Holy Land and the site

8

MATTHEW PARIS'S MAP OF GREAT BRITAIN, C.1250
Detail of Southern England

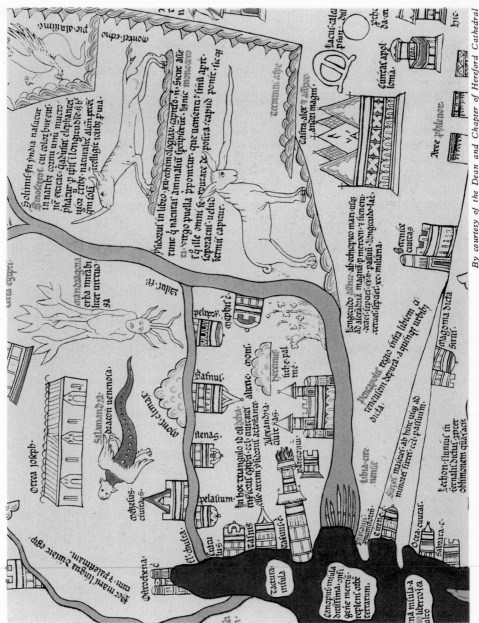

HEREFORD WORLD MAP, c.1280

By courtesy of the Dean and Chapter of Hereford Cathedral

Detail of the Nile Delta

of the Terrestial Paradise, in which men still believed; and the four cardinal points of the compass are marked in the margins, together with the names of the lands opposite them across the seas, such as Norway, Flanders and Normandy. In their choice of symbols and colours to represent the features on their maps Matthew Paris and his successors naturally imitated the style of the dainty miniatures which then adorned all important manuscripts. There already existed, however, some simple pictorial conventions for maps, probably developed by the Graeco-Roman cartographers, which can here be seen in their earliest English form. The sea is green, the rivers and lakes blue, and Snowdon, though it looks like nothing but a pile of crags, is as good a representation of a mountain as any devised by our map-makers during the next three centuries. The towns are indicated by groups of walled and castellated buildings, as they continued to be down to the eighteenth century. The red lines around them may well have been intended to represent roofs of red tiles; this was certainly the reason why, on later maps, all towns are coloured red. The colours were made up from red and white lead, ochre, indigo, verdigris and vegetable juices, and the maps were, of course, drawn upon parchment or dressed sheepskins.

In the Hereford map, so called because it belongs to Hereford Cathedral, there has survived one of the finest and most typical medieval world-maps known. It was drawn about 1306 by Richard of Belleau in Lincolnshire (who was successively prebend of Lincoln, Hereford and Salisbury Cathedrals), and measures about 4 by 5 feet. The map is on parchment, and its details are picked out in fine colours and gold. A rectilinear border of a zig-zag pattern combined with leaves—notable as the earliest known border on an English map—surrounds it, and a large picture of the Last Judgment, with impish devils hauling the damned away, surmounts it. The world, which includes most of Europe and Asia, but only the northern part of Africa, is represented as circular, with a broad band of ocean flowing round it. The east is at the top, and a stately Jerusalem stands, as prescribed by tradition, in the centre.

Although drawn some twenty years after Matthew Paris's death in 1259, the Hereford map takes us back to early mediaeval times. The countries, seas, rivers and mountains are comically misshapen—England not the least—and generally hopelessly misplaced, and the map is covered with a multitude of graphic pictures and written descriptions of monsters and marvels. Here are the wicked giants Gog and Magog, salamanders, phoenixes, lion-bodied gryphons, centaurs, the river Acheron spouting up from the infernal regions, men using their enormous feet as parasols, in fact an intensely interesting world, depicted with great industry. Into these Richard put all his skill with pen and brush, introducing into maps an element of art which in the sixteenth century became extremely prominent. He drew practically all his material, however, from the writings of early geographers, and the Hereford map is therefore valuable only as a rich pictorial record of the geographical beliefs of the Middle Ages.

A single unfinished copy survives of a remarkable map of Great Britain which was drawn about 1335, most probably as a result of the wars of the three Edwards with Wales, Scotland and France (1282-1347). It is called the "Gough Map" after its discoverer, Richard Gough, or the "Bodleian Map" from its present home at Oxford, and is a large coloured map on two parchment skins. From the surprisingly good configuration of our island there can be little doubt that most of England and Wales had been surveyed, although we know nothing of the methods employed. From the time of Euclid (c. 300 B.C.) it had been known that the relative positions of three places could be fixed by measuring the angles made at each by sight-lines to the other two ; but the English had no instruments with which to make these triangulations accurately. The only instruments available for this in 1350 were the magnetic compass and—more commonly used—the astrolabe. The latter, a very ancient instrument, had been perfected by the Arabs, who, from about 800 to 1400 A.D. were the greatest astronomers, navigators and mathematicians in the world. It was already familiar to educated Englishmen in 1387 when Chaucer wrote an excellent treatise upon it for the instruction of his little son. From Chaucer's *Prologue* and from accounts of Royal and judicial progresses it is clear that large numbers of people of all sorts were constantly moving about the country and that there was also considerable traffic in coastal waters, so that the face and shape of England were becoming well-known.

One way of surveying the country was, of course, to plot all its main roads, and this was evidently the chief, though not the only task of the author of the Gough Map. His numerous roads, mediaeval as well as Roman, are shown diagrammatically as straight lines between town and town, but the distances are marked on them. How carefully the unknown author carried this out may be judged from the fact that the same distances are given in road-books published two hundred and fifty years later, in Queen Elizabeth's reign. The little clusters of buildings with red roofs and white walls representing towns are smaller and more artistic than any which preceded them, and the Cathedrals in Canterbury, York, Lincoln and other towns are distinguished by grey lead roofs and tall, brightly coloured steeples surmounted by crosses. Forests, appearing here for the first time on an English map, are each indicated by two graceful little trees, intertwined and coloured green. The author shows all his roads in red, probably by royal command, so that they might be more conspicuous. Scotland is here far richer in counties, towns and natural features than Matthew Paris made it, but it was little known to Englishmen and, like the Hebrides and the Shetland and Orkney Islands, is badly misshapen. The map has the east at the top, and the points of the compass, indications of latitude and longitude and a scale are all lacking, but the names of the

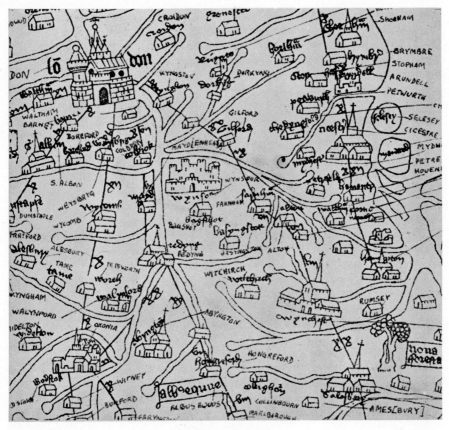

SOUTHERN ENGLAND
From the Gough map of Great Britain, c. 1335

nearest countries, east, south and west, are marked at the edges. Yet, in its design, its construction and its multitudinous details, the Gough map is a real map such as any traveller could use, and a notable achievement for its time. There is evidence that several other copies of the original once existed, and that they were in use, as they deserved to be, as late as 1540.

After 1340 a new kind of map, the estate map, began to appear. By 1400 the monasteries owned well over half the land in the kingdom, and they kept very careful records of their possessions—of manors, farms, warrens, woods, mills and fisheries, and of how every parcel of land was utilized and of the many and complicated services and dues owed them by their tenants. The plan of the great Benedictine Abbey of Chertsey here reproduced, which was drawn about 1432, is a good specimen of the estate plans not only of its time, but of the century that followed. With no scale, and little regard for distance or proportion, and brilliantly coloured, it is as much a picture as a map. Nevertheless the principles of representation and of the use of colours observed by its author are those which, with some modifications, were continued in English maps right down to 1750. The fields, roads and streams are shown in plan, but the buildings and woods in elevation. Ordinary buildings have red roofs, although the monastery itself has a fine leaded roof and spire similar to the cathedrals on the Gough Map. The woods are green, the roads a dirty yellow, which was doubtless their natural colour, and the streams are not only blue, but their currents and eddies are emphasized by a damascene pattern which is found, alternating with flowing current lines, on MS. maps down to about 1570. At that time the fields were measured by wooden poles a perch in length—whence our phrase "perch or pole." The present standard perch of 16½ feet was used, but there was also a perch of only 12 feet, while for wooded land it was always 18 feet long. This map is quite modern in that each field has its name, and, more important, its size in acres, and the use to which it was put, such as meadow or pasture. Its author evidently realised the superiority of wash (thin water-colours) over paint as a medium for colouring maps, and from his time onwards wash came more and more into use.

NAVIGATORS, LANDOWNERS AND ESTATE SURVEYORS
1500-1565

Although the first half of the sixteenth century produced only one notable English map, it was a period of rapid progress in all branches of cartography. This was the result of events abroad. About 1409 Byzantine scholars, flying from the Turks before Constantinople, had brought to Italy manuscript copies of the maps in Claudius Ptolemy's *Cosmographia*, drawn about 168 A.D. at Alexandria. The greatest work of the Greek geographers, these formed not only the first atlas of the world but laid down for map-makers of all time the principles for the construction of maps of large areas upon a network of lines of latitude and longitude (parallels and meridians). Englishmen who, their minds fired by the New Learning, travelled abroad in ever increasing numbers after 1520, brought back an enthusiasm for the study of geography and cartography aroused by Ptolemy's work and by contact with the Continental scholars who were continuing it, as well as a knowledge of the new devices for navigation, for surveying and for printing maps from copper plates which the Age of Discovery had inspired Continental mathematicians and instrument-makers to invent. Henry VIII was himself a product of the Renascence in his talent for

MS. COASTAL CHART OF WALBERSWICK AND BAWDSEY, C. 1540

music and poetry, his skill in feats of arms and his ruthless and unscrupulous despotism; but he had a breadth of vision which was invaluable to a country as backward as England. English seamen were far behind those of Portugal, Spain and France as navigators. In 1520 they still possessed no sea-charts except a very few drawn by foreigners, and though, like Chaucer's Shipman from Dartmouth, they "knew well alle the havens as they were from Gotland to the Cape of Finistere" and round it into the Mediterranean, all their sailing was coastwise. Henry set about introducing skilled navigators and mathematicians, mainly from northern France, to instruct his pilots in nautical science. In 1514 he founded the historic Brethren of the Trinity to aid coastal mariners with pilots, beacons, landmarks and buoys. Moreover he had MS. charts made of many English harbours, from the Bristol Channel round to Newcastle.

The originals of a few of these charts—the first, so far as we know, ever made by Englishmen—as well as copies of others, are still preserved in the British Museum and other great libraries. They are really bird's eye views of the ports, taken from a little way out at sea. Drawn upon parchment, which for maps was still preferred to paper, they are highly coloured with wash or paint. In the foreground a graceful ship is generally found riding, with shoals, sandbanks and varying sea depths marked around it, the depths being given in fathoms; beyond it the nature of the shore—sandy beach, shingle beach, rocks or cliffs—is graphically depicted in plan, cliffs being, as it were, rolled back to show their faces, and boulders being often greatly exaggerated in size; and behind this,

13

represented in elevation, are the landmarks by which the mariner could steer his course, such as church-towers, beacons, windmills and lone trees. These charts were intended to be used in conjunction with "Rutters," or books of sailing directions.

By his dissolution of the monasteries between 1536 and 1540 and his grants of a large proportion of their vast estates to laymen, Henry VIII created a new landed gentry. Few of them belonged to the old noble families, which had been greatly reduced by attainder, execution and death in battle ; most of them were able business men, interested in making a profit from their new possessions and many had written surveys made of their lands. This gradually brought into existence a body of professional lay surveyors, distinct from the manorial stewards. The "surveyors" so-called were authorities and advisors upon manorial law and estate management, enjoyed a certain prestige and did not make maps ; the men who measured parcels of land and laid down boundaries were called "landmeters" and had little professional standing. At first their methods were those of simple geometrical mensuration with a cord measuring a fixed number of perches in length and soaked in resin to prevent it from shrinking. The first English work on the subject, *The Maner of Measurynge of Lande*, was published about 1537, soon after the dissolution of the monasteries had begun, and the author, Richard de Benese, had been an Augustinian Canon but was evidently well able to adapt himself to altered circumstances.

The discovery that maps could be printed from engraved copper plate had been made in Italy about 1473, and in 1477 the maps of Ptolemy's *Cosmographia*—the first ever engraved in copper—were published in Bologna. The marvellous opportunities, cartographical, artistic and commercial, presented by this new invention were quickly realized ; and as popular interest in travel, new markets abroad and geography increased, as it did rapidly in a world which was expanding intellectually no less than physically, engraved maps became almost as important an educative medium as printed books. The first important engraved map of England, apart from those in editions of Ptolemy's *Cosmographia*, was one of Great Britain and Ireland published at Rome in 1546. The author was George Lily, a member of the household of the exiled Cardinal de la Pole ; the map was engraved through the efforts of a group of English Catholic refugees at Rome.

This map, with its firm but delicate lines, its stately ornamental panels or "cartouches" enclosing the title and descriptive texts, and its clear, sloping Italic lettering, must have been a revelation to Englishmen. It is uncoloured, for the Italian map-engravers wisely eschewed colours as likely to conceal important details ; so that for the representation of all features it depends on symbols or conventions developed to replace colours. The sea is stippled, and enlivened with dainty ships and huge monsters ; the coast-line is emphasized with hatching ; the forests are groups of

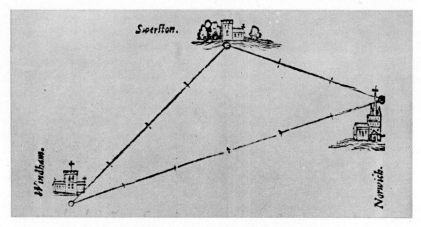

AN ILLUSTRATION OF EARLY TRIANGULATION
From W. Cuningham's *Cosmographical Glasse*, 1559

bushy trees, slightly shaded on the right ; the lower hills are gently curving lines with shading added on one side, but mountain ranges are depicted like so many sugar-loaves. Small, neat groups of buildings represent towns, but a tiny circle below each indicates its centre, for measuring distances, "Measure from the prick in everi town," says a contemporary MS. The symbols for metropolitan, episcopal and county towns and for castles are explained at the bottom of the map, thus beginning the "Tables" of symbols or conventional signs which have appeared on all good maps ever since. Curiously enough, no roads are shown, though other facts show that Lily utilized a copy of the Gough map. The influence of Ptolemy and of recent progress in cartography is evident in that the map is oriented to the North and that degrees of latitude and longitude are marked in a double-lined border around it. There is also a scale in the form of a handsome engraved rule divided into 200 Roman or Italian miles. The latitudes are not very far wrong, but England is shown as lying between 14°35′ and 24°30′ East longitude. This was the result of the acceptance by most contemporary geographers of a prime meridian drawn through the island of St. Mary in the Azores because there, at the time, there was little or no declination of the magnetic needle from the true North, although everywhere else the declination was noted to vary greatly. The representation of Scotland and of the Scottish islands is extremely good, far superior to anything earlier. It was probably based upon a chart drawn by Alexander Lindsay when he was chief pilot of an expedition round the Scottish coasts which James V made in 1540. Ireland, however is hardly recognisable. After Lily's return to England, copies of the map were printed at London in 1555.

It was to Flemish technicians that the English of the mid-sixteenth century owed most of their education in map-making. The ancient friendship between the two countries had become closer than ever, and Mercator, one of the greatest geographers of all time, was a Fleming. About 1533, a professor at Louvain, Gemma of Friesland, surveyed a large area between Mechlin and Antwerp by triangulation. His method, which was really compass-sketching, was generally adopted everywhere during the next twenty years. In his book, *The Cosmographical Glasse* (1559) William Cuningham of Norwich described a similar triangulation made by him between Norwich, Swarston and Wymondham. Already, however, the planimetrum and other similar instruments were giving way practically everywhere to the plane-table. This, as most people know, is a light rectangular wooden table on which the surveyor could lay his paper, holding his alidade, or sighted ruler, in position over it while sighting and drawing, and only using a compass when commencing his map to fix his ray to the magnetic North. The better educated surveyors were quick to add knowledge of mapping with a plane-table to their knowledge of the laws and management of property, and the Royal surveyors, usually employed as engineers to fortify castles and harbours against the Scots and the French, extended their activities to surveying and drawing maps of districts of military importance and of property escheated to the Crown. A few of these are still preserved.

By 1564, the year of Shakespeare's birth, a group of young Elizabethans, men like William Camden, Philip Sidney's friend, were discovering, like the Italians of the Renascence, the history, antiquities and literature of their own country with pride and delight. Their eagerness to see her cities and shires mapped was fanned by the publication in 1564 of a fine map of England and Wales by Gerard Mercator, based in the main upon information supplied by Englishmen such as the energetic and versatile Dr. John Dee. By 1570 the number of skilled English surveyors had greatly increased. Lord Secretary Cecil, the watch-dog of England, had caused MS. maps to be made, for his own use, of Ireland, where there was constant fighting, and of the northern English counties, where the Catholic Rising of the North had just been quelled; while Richard Popinjay, a government surveyor, had mapped parts of southern England. Some of the new nobles, among them the Earl of Pembroke, one of Henry VIII's innumerable connexions by marriage, who had obtained large grants of land at Wilton, began to have plans made of their estates.

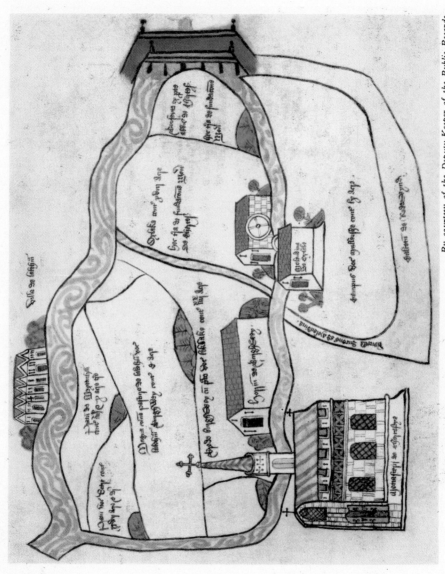

MS PLAN OF CHERTSEY ABBEY, 1432
From the Cartulary of Chertsey Abbey

By courtesy of the Deputy-Keeper of the Public Records

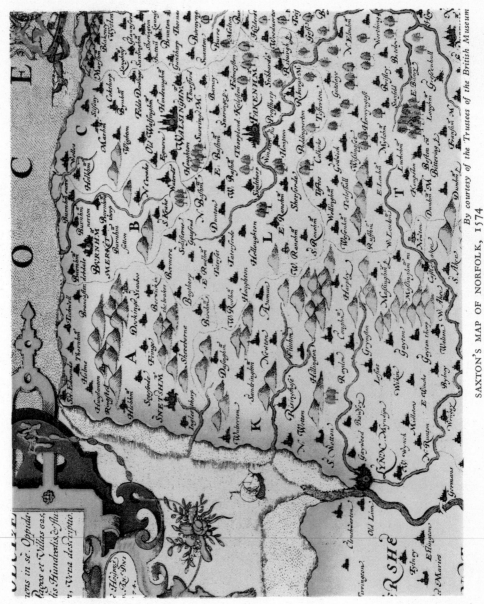

SAXTON'S MAP OF NORFOLK, 1574   By courtesy of the Trustees of the British Museum
Detail of N.W. portion

By 1570 the Flemings, partly owing to their skill in copper-engraving, had supplanted the Italians as the chief purveyors of maps to the world, and their cartographical knowledge was being brought to England by Protestants flying from the persecution of the Spaniards. In that year Abraham Ortelius of Antwerp published his historic atlas of the world, which was acclaimed by the cultured Englishmen who had begun to study cosmography and geography. In 1571 the most important work of the century on surveying appeared, the *Pantometria* of Leonard Digges, published by his son Thomas. Digges brought order and mathematical accuracy into the existing methods of surveying and mensuration, and described a new instrument of his own invention, the "Topographicall Instrument." In principle it closely resembled our modern theodolite, and was soon called by that name, though some time elapsed before it came into manufacture and general use.

The first map known to have been engraved on copper in England was one of Palestine, which appeared, fittingly enough, in the first edition of the "Bishops' Bible." It was the work of Humphrey Cole, a goldsmith employed in the Mint and a famous instrument-maker. In style it resembles Lily's map, but the cartouche combines a lozenge-shaped Italian "strap-work" design with decorations of birds, fruits, flowers and snakes, which reveal Flemish love of ornament for its own sake. The conventional symbols are unchanged except that the rivers have flowing lines along their courses and the mountains are definitely shaded on the eastern side, a convention thenceforward generally followed. With the possible exception of a view of Norwich included in Cuningham's *Cosmographical Glasse* (1559), the first English town to be engraved on copper was Cambridge (1572), executed by Richard Lyne. It is a bird's-eye plan-profile in the style of the fifteenth century, and a charming picture. An obscure young surveyor from Yorkshire, Christopher Saxton, was, however, the man destined to carry out the national atlas towards which all these developments were working. About 1573 Thomas Seckford, a wealthy Suffolk gentleman and one of the Queen's Masters of Requests, commissioned Saxton to make maps of all the English counties, which he undertook to have engraved and published at his own expense. There is strong evidence that Seckford originally intended the atlas to accompany and illustrate Raphael Holinshed's famous *Chronicles of England, Irelande and Scotland*, which was then in preparation; but eventually he published it independently.

Saxton's first two maps were engraved in 1574, others appeared in rapid succession, and the atlas, containing a general map of England and thirty-four county maps, was completed in 1579. The Queen had early become interested, with the result that the Royal Tudor arms, a lion and a dragon, appeared on every map.

To survey and map single-handed the whole of England and Wales in six years would have been at that time a superhuman feat, and there is no doubt that Saxton had many MS. maps lent to him by men like John Wolfe, the publisher of Holinshed's *Chronicles*, who had collected several maps which were never printed, and William Lambarde, the antiquary. These he needed only to check and correct as he travelled about, generally on horseback. Nothing is recorded about his method of survey, but he must have made compass-sketches or used a plane-table from eminences, for he had an open letter from the Queen to local mayors and Justice Shallows, ordering them to assist him and guide him to any "Towre, Castle or hill to view that countrey." The small counties he mapped three, or even four, on one sheet, larger counties had a sheet to themselves, and Yorkshire, his own county and the largest, had a double sheet. The scales vary, therefore, from $1\frac{3}{4}$ to $3\frac{3}{4}$ miles to an inch. Many "customary" miles, which varied considerably in different districts, were then in use, for the confusion of surveyors; but Saxton seems to have employed, whenever possible, the Old English mile of 2240 yards. The Hundreds, then the chief administrative unit, are shown in only five of the counties, their limits being marked by dotted lines. Thenceforward it became usual to mark the boundaries of the Hundreds in colour. Considering how much travelling he had to do and that at least one road-book with distances had already been published, it is strange that Saxton omitted all roads. To engrave the maps Seckford was fortunate in finding a number of Protestant Flemish refugees, such as Remy Hogenberg and Leonard Terwoort of Antwerp. Their cartouches and Royal Arms are in the ornate, sometimes fantastic style of the Flemish schools; but their general style also illustrates that love of display which characterized Elizabeth and her courtiers. The first issues of these maps were a blaze of colours with gold added in some cases; while the groups of flowers, fruits, birds, animals and fish which overloaded Terwoort's cartouches and the insipid Neptunes, nereids and cherubs which decorated Hogenberg's had their counterpart in the pageants arranged by Elizabeth's favourites for the entertainment of their Gloriana. The colours were in wash and were put on by hand, generally in the publisher's shop though sometimes and inartistically, by the purchasers themselves. They were the old manuscript conventional colours for topographical features, revived under Flemish influence. A few of the maps dated 1576 to 1579 were engraved by Englishmen, notably by Augustine Ryther, one of our finest map engravers, who always signed himself "Anglus" to show that he was not a foreigner.

Apart from the cartouches, the decorations included narrow borders imitating carved and painted wooden frames, monsters and ships in the

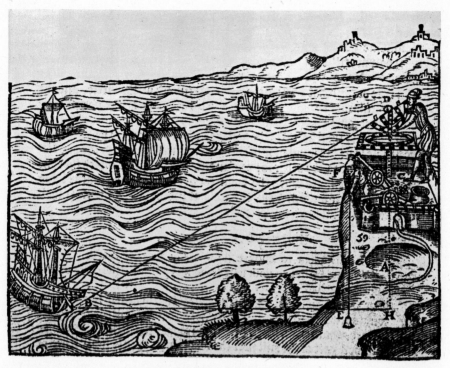

THE USE OF THE THEODOLITE
From L. Digges' *Pantometria*, 1571

sea, the arms of Seckford as well as those of the Queen, a large brass
compass-divider surmounting the scale, and a very ornamental scale rule.
The only new conventional sign is a paling surrounding a piece of land,
representing the great parks which the new nobility had enclosed, largely
from the common parish lands—"whereby the inhabitants of many places
were devoured." Mountains are like coloured sugar-loaves, giving no
idea either of height or of gradient and often so large that villages lying
among them had to be misplaced to be made visible. While villages are
represented by a single church tower, towns of any importance have two
or more, and cities several. The flowing Italic hand, which, in various
styles, had reached England in the "writing books" of foreign copper
engravers, and was recognized by Malvolio as "the sweet Roman hand,"
is seen in its most beautiful forms. Saxton introduced a system of lettering,
such as we use nowadays, to indicate the relative importance of the different
features. Small Italic, either current or printing style, is used for small
places, larger and bolder Italics for towns, and also for forests, chases,

19

moors and mountain ranges, while large towns and Hundreds are proclaimed in Italic capitals of two kinds.

Saxton's general map of England and Wales in the atlas, engraved by Ryther was, both artistically and cartographically, a masterpiece ; and a larger map by him published, again at Seckford's expense, in 1583, remained the most authoritative map of England for the next century. Both, like all maps of the time, were drawn upon the crude conical projection first devised by Ptolemy, and each shows degrees and minutes of latitude and longitude in the margins. The prime meridian was still drawn through St. Mary's in the Azores, although it was known that true North and magnetic North no longer coincided there. The scale on each of these maps gives three different miles, called "Long, Middle, Short." They were all "customary" miles, the "short" being about 2035 yards long.

Saxton's atlas was the first national atlas produced by any country, and Saxton deserves a place beside Shakespeare as an interpreter of the national consciousness, unity and pride which were the greatest achievements of Elizabethan England. Moreover it established cartography firmly in England, partly because it showed how engraved maps could be printed in large numbers. As late as 1600 copies from the original plates were being printed and sold. These were often uncoloured, and were weak impressions, as the designs on the plates were wearing down. Their style at once became the model both for draftsmen and engravers, setting a standard even for MS., estate maps, which from 1580 onwards were generally as artistic as any engraved county maps.

The maps of John Norden were more original than any which preceded or followed them for a long time, and embodied that spirit of independent scientific research which arose among English University men of the middle classes in the 1590's. He had a grandiose scheme for a new atlas of England, the *Speculum Britanniae*, which would contain archaeological and historical descriptions of each county ; but from lack of patronage only succeeded in publishing maps of five counties and plans of London and Westminster (1593-98), although he prepared other counties in MS. Always poor, he was an indefatigable worker, surveying and drawing MS. maps of estates all over the country, including those of the Duchy of Cornwall and the Honor of Windsor, besides publishing two valuable books on surveying, an excellent road-book (1625), and—for he was both a pious man and a surveyor—eleven devotional works. The maps of the *Speculum* contain many features new in England, though some of them originated on the Continent. Thus they were the first engraved English maps to show roads—represented by double dotted lines. Instead of ornamental borders, double lines surround the maps, containing figures along the top and letters down one side which give references, such as are familiar to everybody to-day, for finding any place on the map ; while the inner line is divided into fractions of an inch, supplying a simple marginal scale.

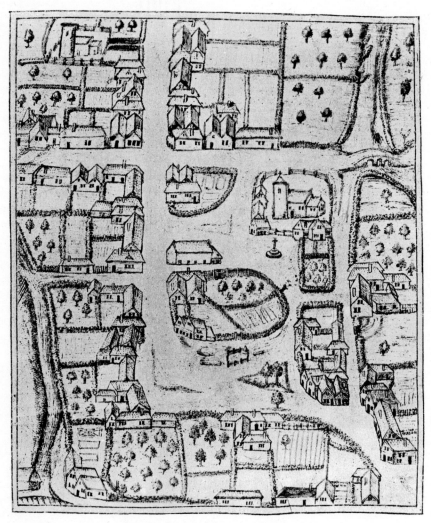

THE VILLAGE OF WILTON, WILTSHIRE
Drawn c. 1563 for a survey of the Estates of William, 1st Earl of Pembroke

Norden was the first Englishman to introduce a symbol for a battle, representing the Battle of Barnet by two opposed ranks of little swordsmen. The symbol now in use—two crossed swords—probably derives from his. His antiquarian zeal led him indeed to include on his maps tables of symbols for many curious things, for "Howses of gent.; Nob; men's howses ; Howses and places of Quene Eli. ; Decayde places." The houses of nobility and gentry were no doubt marked partly to attract interest and purchasers among the right people ; and each map bears the coat of arms of some patron who paid for its engraving and printing. Saxton, Norden and their successors depended upon patrons for their work and livelihood, and for the next two hundred years the seats and coats of arms of influential persons were hopefully engraved upon nearly all maps printed for public sale. Norden also introduced into England the triangular tables of distances between towns which were later adopted on most road maps, especially those intended for commercial travellers.

After 1580 MS. maps became very numerous, including plans of towns, estate plans, and many maps of coastal districts and harbours carried out for the government. Ralph Aggas executed some fine estate maps, while the plans of Robert Adams, a Royal surveyor, are perhaps the most delicate and lovely ever drawn in this country. Some plans of the coastal defences and beacons hastily erected in 1585 against the arrival of the Spanish Armada are still preserved. On one of these, showing Waborne in Norfolk, the draftsman wrote "Reason would a scale but tyme permits not." Of the few town plans which were engraved in England, Exeter (1587) by Remy Hogenberg and Oxford (1588) by Aggas, engraved by Ryther, are outstanding. London of course attracted many artists and surveyors but a large plan, probably by Aggas, with much fascinating detail, which was published about 1592, is considered the best representation of Elizabethan London. Maps of Wales and Scotland appeared soon after the introduction of map-engraving into England. That of Scotland published in 1578 by John Leslie, Bishop of Ross, was scarcely more than a reduced copy of Lily's map of 1546 ; but Humphrey Lhuyd, the Welsh antiquary, contributed a good map of his country to an edition of Ortelius' atlas issued at Antwerp in 1573, and Saxton utilized it. In Ireland MS. maps were drawn of several confiscated territories, but being official documents, were not published. A large and detailed map of Ireland was, however, published in 1599, the author being Baptista Boazio, who had accompanied the Earl of Essex on his rash expedition thither. Like its predecessors, it represents the west coast as running practically due north-south. This error on earlier maps had misled several of the captains of the defeated Armada into setting a course due south for Spain after they had rounded Teelin Head in Donegal, with the result that many ships were wrecked on the rock-bound coasts of Mayo and Galway.

Although they knew their own coasts well, English seamen possessed very few detailed charts. Indeed the Flemish and Dutch, from their long experience as enterprising sea-traders, knew the waters of Northern Europe better than any Englishman ; and it was a Dutchman, Lucas Waghenaer, who gave the world the earliest volume of engraved charts, published in 1583. It depicted the coasts from Stockholm to Cadiz

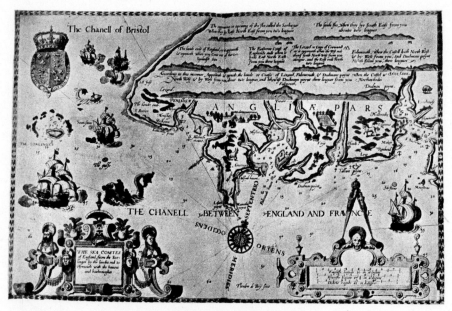

SOUTH-WEST COAST OF ENGLAND
From L. Waghenaer's *Mariners' Mirrour*, 1588

except those of Ireland, Wales and western and northern Scotland. Admiral Lord Howard of Effingham at once perceived its value, especially as he knew that Philip II was already contemplating an invasion of England from the sea, and he persuaded Sir Anthony Ashley to translate it. The translation, entitled *The Mariners' Mirrour*, with charts copied from Waghenaer's, appeared in 1588 shortly before the Armada sailed, and must have gladdened the hearts of Effingham's captains. Waghenaer's charts are a development of the earlier MS. coastal views. Shoals, banks, shingle-beaches and soundings are marked clearly, and good anchorages indicated by the figure of an anchor. Wherever the shore is steep or there are landmarks upon it, these are bent backwards, as it were, so that they appear in elevation, although the sea and land beside them are in plan. A new and important addition was made at the top of each chart—a silhouette of the coast as seen from two or three leagues out at sea. These silhouettes, which derived from the views in the early sailing-books, are a standard feature on our present Admiralty charts. So well known did this work become that for the next century and a half English sailors usually called any volume of charts a "Waggoner."

The rich territories and richer trade which the Portuguese and Spaniards consolidated for themselves in America, the Indies and Africa during the

23

sixteenth century aroused an eager though commercial interest in world geography among the English. Of the maps and charts of the world which inspired the colonizing schemes of men like Dr. John Dee, Frobisher and Raleigh, none can compare with the great globes completed in 1592, which are still preserved in the Library of the Middle Temple. These, one terrestial and one celestial, were fashioned by Emery Molyneux, an instrument-maker ; elliptical strips, or gores, were engraved by a Fleming, Josse de Hondt or Jodocus Hondius ; and the expenses were borne by William Sanderson, a London merchant and a patron of Norden. At least three great Elizabethan geographers contributed to make the terrestial globe as correct as possible—Edward Wright, a Fellow of Caius College and our first exponent of nautical mathematics, John Davis, who had already made three voyages in search of the North-West passage, and Richard Hakluyt, probably the greatest force behind the expansion of the English overseas.

English captains such as Frobisher in 1576 and Drake in 1577 had generally carried globes with them when venturing upon ocean voyages because they had no satisfactory charts. Of the ocean charts in use, one, the commoner, showed no parallels and none except the prime meridian, but was covered with compass-roses from which lines radiated and intersected everywhere. These straight lines were "true bearings" on the flat surface of the chart, but were nothing of the kind on the spherical surface of our world, and gave little help to sailors attempting to keep a constant course across an ever curving ocean. Charts drawn upon conical and "equidistant" or cylindrical projections proved equally misleading ; but in 1599 Edward Wright solved the problem with a famous world-chart, *A True Hydrographicall Description of the World*. It was based upon a chart published by the great Mercator in 1569, in which, though the meridians did not converge but were equidistant, the scale along them was increased gradually towards the Poles to compensate for the increased scale along the parallels North and South of the Equator. On this every straight line was a constant bearing. While, however, Mercator left no explanation of his method, Wright worked out the mathematical problems involved and gave data enabling any trained navigator to ensure that a correct sailing course or "rhumb line" would be straight. Ever since then most ocean charts have been constructed on Mercator's, or rather, Wright's projection. On Wright's chart and on all which followed it down to about 1700, longitude was always reckoned eastwards, never westwards, so that a point 5° W. of the prime meridian was entered as in Longitude 355°. This was probably due to the influence of Ptolemy, who knew nothing west of his prime meridian, which was drawn through the Canaries.

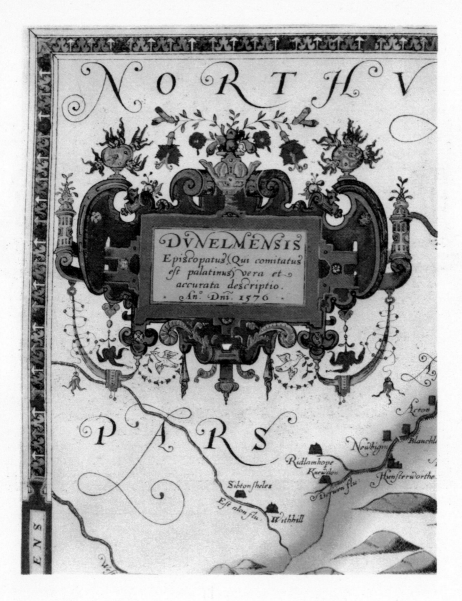

CARTOUCHE BY A. RYTHER ON SAXTON'S MAP OF DURHAM, 1576
By courtesy of the Trustees of the British Museum

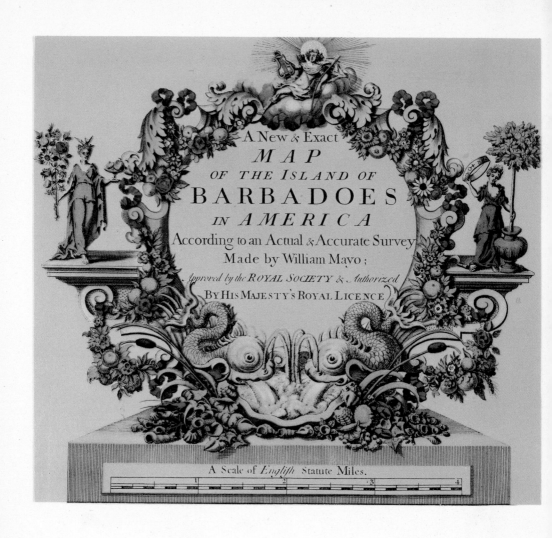

A New & Exact
MAP
OF THE ISLAND OF
BARBADOES
IN AMERICA
According to an Actual & Accurate Survey
Made by William Mayo;
Approved by the ROYAL SOCIETY & Authorized
BY HIS MAJESTY'S ROYAL LICENCE

A Scale of *English* Statute Miles.

CARTOUCHE ON W. MAYO'S MAP OF BARBADOS, 1722
By courtesy of the Trustees of the British Museum

PUBLISHERS, PURITANS AND DUTCH BAROQUE
1601-1660

In 1601 there appeared a figure destined to dominate English carto-graphy for two and a half centuries—the publisher. Between 1601 and 1603 copies of a map of the British Isles and large, well-engraved maps of twelve of the counties were issued for sale here. Most of them bore neither imprint nor date, but it is fairly certain that they were engraved and printed at Antwerp and published by Hans Woutneel, a Flemish engraver living in London and a friend of Ortelius. Though copied almost literally from Saxton's and Norden's maps, they were uniform in that the roads and the Hundreds were shown on all, and some of Norden's symbols adopted. English publishers soon joined in. An edition of William Camden's well-known *Britannia*, a monument of patriotic learning, was issued in 1607 with a full set of county maps copied again—except Pembrokeshire—from those of Saxton and Norden, though with the ornament, colours and Norden's roads omitted. Since they bear Saxton's and Norden's names, these are often mistaken for originals, though their small size and crowded features should make that error impossible. Many of them are beautifully engraved by William Hole, who was also the first Englishman to engrave music.

The *Theatre of the Empire of Great Britaine*, by John Speed, first published in 1611-12, is the best known of early English atlases. Speed was a prosperous member of the Company of Merchant Taylors whose recreations were drawing maps, writing devotional books and studying history. He came to the notice of Fulk Greville, Philip Sidney's friend, who paid him a stipend to write a *History of Great Britaine*. The *Theatre* was originally only intended to illustrate the *History*, but the part proved greater than the whole and the *History* is deservedly forgotten. Nearly all the maps were close copies of those of Saxton and Norden, with the addition "Performed by John Speed." His performance consisted mainly in covering the face of each county map with the coats of arms of notables who had borne a county title and with historical and antiquarian engravings and legends, and filling the margins of the general maps of the four countries with useful costume figures of their nobility, gentry and peasants. Yet he introduced two valuable innovations which were adopted by most of his successors—delightful little plans of the county towns inset on the face of each map, and a historical description, like those already usual on Continental maps, printed on the back. These plans, many of which have not yet been traced to their sources, are perhaps—when uncoloured—the best things published in a period of decline in English cartography. Speed drew upon every available source of infor-mation, revising Saxton's Norfolk, Cheshire and Leicestershire from notes obtained from local antiquaries, and printing maps of the Isles of Man and Wight which had been drawn much earlier by Thomas Durham and William White. Ireland and Scotland he wisely copied from the best maps extant, those in Mercator's *Atlas* of 1595. These he obtained direct from Amsterdam; for though published in London the whole of the *Theatre* was engraved and printed at Amsterdam by Jodocus Hondius (Josse de Hondt). During his exile in London (c. 1584-94) Hondius had realised the commercial possibilities in maps, and, among other maps, he had engraved a magnificent chart of Drake's circumnavigation of the world. About 1594 he moved to Amsterdam, took over Mercator's great cartographical establishment and became by 1609 the leading map publisher in the world. As English engravers were rare (Augustine Ryther is last heard of as a prisoner in the Tower in 1595) and no publisher possessed the copper-plates and presses necessary for a work as large as the *Theatre*, Speed naturally turned to him.

The publication of the *Theatre* began a new era in English cartography. Publishers had early discovered both that a copper plate, once engraved, could be used over a long period, and that the public would always buy new maps whether there was anything new in them or not. Consequently for well over a century the plates of Saxton's and Speed's maps were used by a succession of publishers for reprints on which only the imprint, date and sometimes the dedication and cartouche were altered. Thus we cannot tell which edition of Speed Pepys used when, in 1662, looking for timber for the Navy, he "turned to the Forest of Deane in Speede's Mapps, and there showed me how it lies." Certainly the reissue of Saxton's atlas in 1645, of Speed's in 1646 and the publication of a careful copy of Saxton's large map of England in 1644—"Useful for all Cõmanders for quarteringe of Souldiers"—were all intended for impartial sale to both sides in the Civil War. These atlases had however to compete with serious rivals, which are still found in many English bookshops. While the absolutism of the Stuarts was dragging England into civil war, the Dutch Republic was strengthening her hold on an overseas empire which brought her enormous wealth, and securing a virtual monopoly of the world's maritime trade. And by 1640 the Dutch, who were good business men as well as good artists, were supplying the whole world with fine atlases, maps and charts and noble volumes of engraved views and plans. By 1650 the two greatest cartographical publishers in the world, Joan Blaeu and Jan Janszoon, were selling rival versions of Speed's county maps in their atlases. No copyright law existed, and everybody copied everybody else's maps ungrudgingly. Without altering them basically the Dutch engravers transformed Speed's motley crowd of images into clear and artistic maps. The few single maps of this period, most of them published in connection with speculative "projects" for land reclamation, mines, mills and water-works, were generally characterized by poor engraving, mean lettering and absence of ornament and colour.

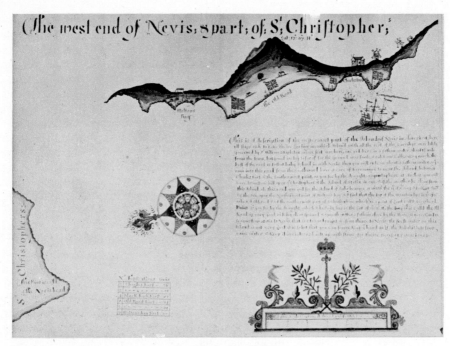

ST. KITTS AND NEVIS
Ms. Chart by William Hack, c. 1687

Manuscript estate maps multiplied fast after 1603, for many wealthy merchants were setting up as country gentlemen, institutions like the Oxford and Cambridge Colleges were looking into the boundaries and rents of their widespread properties and disputes over the enclosure of common lands were increasing. Many of these were evidently surveyed by 'Plaine Tablers' such as one described by Ralph Aggas, "Mary, he was a plumber and had learned from a Painter : in less than an acre and a halfe he fel short at his cloaze by two perches at least."

After 1630 many estate maps were enlivened by pictures of people ploughing or cutting corn in the fields, of cattle and horses grazing, and of carts and horsemen on the roads. These were probably inserted, not for ornament, but to distinguish arable land from pasture and high roads from lanes. Practically all surveyors continued to use "customary" miles of various lengths, but Edmund Gunter's chain of 22 yards came into use about 1624. The Elizabethan colour conventions were still observed, Folkingham writing "Trees may have a sadder Greene, composed of White Lead and Verdigreece." Roads were marked on none of these maps except Woutneel's and the MS. maps.

27

The work in the sea-charts begun by Waghenaer in 1583 was continued by his countrymen, and their great sea-atlases, published from 1612 onwards, were the mainstay of mariners of all countries. The few English charts which have survived were the work of explorers or of exiles. We have a fine chart on Mercator's projection of Henry Hudson's last, and fatal, voyage in search of the North West Passage, which shows the legendary Atlantic islands of Frisland and Buss, and a MS. chart of Hudson's Bay and Strait drawn on a conical projection by William Baffin in 1615. By far the greatest of early English chart-makers was however Robert Dudley. A son of Queen Elizabeth's favourite, the Earl of Leicester, by the widowed Lady Sheffield, he failed to prove his legitimacy, and in 1605 left England in disgust to spend the rest of his life in Florence. His *Arcano del Mare* ("The Secret of the Sea") a maritime atlas of the whole world, came out in 1646-47, just before his death. In many ways it was a century before its time. It was the first sea atlas in which every chart was on Mercator's projection, the first to give the magnetic declination of a large number of places, and the first to show the prevailing winds and currents at all important harbours and anchorages. His magnetic declinations are however unreliable. The engraving is superb. Handsome compass roses, ships and little anchors are abundant, soundings are marked, and the coasts are shaded inwards, an improvement, at least for charts, on the usual custom of hatching outwards. Large engravings of the surveying and navigational instruments—the best of their day—used or designed by Dudley are included, giving the work additional value.

SURVEYORS
Ornament on T. Martyn's Map of Cornwall, 1749

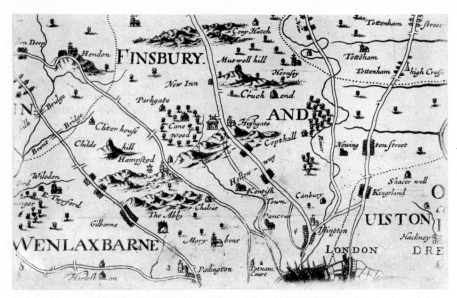

DETAIL FROM JOHN OGILBY'S MAP OF MIDDLESEX, c. 1677

NEW ROADS AND LATE BAROQUE
1660-1760

Under the first Stuarts and the Commonwealth the English people had learned, from hard experience, to think for themselves. The Restoration brought in an age of scientific experiment, led by the Royal Society, and released at the same time an energy as manifold as it was extraordinary in a nation of less than six million souls. England had broken the supremacy of the Dutch both on the sea and in America when, in 1670, John Ogilby challenged their supremacy in cartography. His maps of Kent, Essex and Middlesex, 1670-78, though small, revived Norden's cartographical principles. They showed roads in double lines and hamlets as small circles, there was a marginal index and many special symbols for Post-towns and the like set out in "a Table." In Middlesex villages are denoted by the familiar church and circle in elevation, but towns are represented in a manner which marks the transition from elevation to plan. They are shown as groups of houses by the roadside with their gabled fronts facing upwards. This curious method was sometimes used later on estate plans to show the classic Palladian façades of gentlemen's houses. Except on the ornamentation and on the boundaries of counties and Hundreds, colours were abandoned, as it was realized both that they obscured the details on maps and that they tended to rot the

29

paper. Important features were distinguished by Roman letters instead of Italic, capitals of three sizes being used, though cursive Italics were retained for minor features.

Ogilby was aware that such maps would hardly help travellers. Yet although a large part of the nation had begun to travel, knowledge of the roads was so localized that guides were needed for every stage, his inn-keepers often acting in that capacity for Pepys. As skilled a surveyor as Norden, Ogilby had more organizing ability, for he had been in turn a fashionable dancing master, Master of the King's Revels in Ireland, a translator of Homer and Virgil and a publisher. In 1675 he published *Britannia, Volume I* in which, on 100 large plates, all the roads of England and Wales were engraved to a scale of one inch to a mile. Such a road-atlas had never been produced, hardly imagined, in any country, and in interest and clearness the maps surpass our modern motoring maps. The main roads all start from the Standard at Cornhill in London, and are carried outwards on continuous strip-maps which depict not only all the cross-roads, bridges, hills and county boundaries to be crossed but diverse objects by the wayside. Legends such as "Enter a moore," "A Gibbit" and "The Porcupine Inn" tell the traveller just what to expect. Dots along the roads indicate furlongs, enclosed roads are distinguished from open and a compass-rose accompanies every strip. The *Britannia* was the first engraved atlas in which the statute mile was used throughout. The road distances had been measured by an army of surveyors using "Peram-bulators" or wheels on which every revolution was registered as on a modern cyclometer.

The value of Ogilby's roads was at once realized, and thenceforward no maps were without roads. The *Britannia* itself was four times re-published, and a crowd of road-atlases and road-maps based upon it but reduced to handy sizes appeared from 1700 on to 1794. Even Saxton's atlas, his large map of England and Speed's *Theatre* re-appeared in 1676-87 with roads added.

After 1675 the history of English cartography becomes to a great extent the history of publishers and of the gradual incorporation into their maps and charts of advances in geography, geodesy, hydrography, survey-ing, engraving, representative symbols, lettering, decorative art and colouring. Between 1680 and 1715 their publications quickly came to include atlases as well as single maps, issued in every size and in ever increasing volume. At first some of them stole information and copied maps, their most useful quarry being the atlases of the Dutch and French; but from 1690 onwards original developments of many kinds appeared. Surveys, small and sporadic but all contributing to give a more accurate image of the country, were carried out and useful information supplied, by local estate surveyors. After 1700 colour disappeared from the orna-ments on maps, and was continued only on boundaries. More important

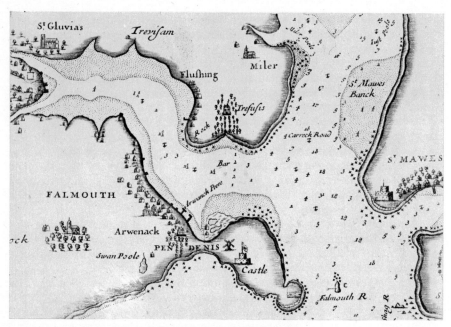

FALMOUTH AND ST. MAWES
From G. Collins' *Great Britain's Coasting Pilot*, 1693

was the substitution of the meridian of St. Paul's for that of the Azores as the prime meridian. The earliest known map with this meridian is one of Hertfordshire published by John Seller in 1676, although the idea hardly originated with Seller. In fact, Charles II had founded the Royal Observatory at Greenwich in 1675 to settle the vexed questions of longitude, and Flamsteed, the first Astronomer Royal, fixed his sighting-arc along that meridian; but probably national interest in the rebuilding of St. Paul's determined the choice. Together with degrees and minutes of longitude, minutes of time east and west of the meridian were marked in the horizontal margins of many maps down to 1725; reference squares on maps, with marginal letters, were common. In 1721 John Senex substituted for the time-honoured Ptolemaic scale, "English miles, 60 to 1 Degree" (of latitude), "English measured miles, 69½ to a Degree," which is not far wrong for statute miles.

For a long time there was little uniformity in symbols for towns and villages. Ogilby wrote in his *Britannia*, "Capital towns are described Ichnographically" or in plan, "and all other buildings Scenographically or in prospect," that is, in elevation; but from 1678 to 1754 cities were generally represented either in plan or as little groups of towers, market

31

towns and large villages by the customary church towers with circles, hamlets by plain circles. The towers were often poor, but some were very artistic, throwing long shadows eastwards as if they were bathed in soft afternoon sunshine. Hills were often similarly depicted. Left clear white on their western side, they look small and alluring, though in fact neither their height, slopes nor exact position is defined. Besides engraved Roman capitals, Roman printed letters came into use for the names of small towns. As time went on symbols were inserted for everything— cities, shire towns, market towns, judges' circuits, bishoprics, medicinal waters, Roman stations, charity schools (a ✠) and different kinds of mills. Rectories and vicarages were distinguished by the letters R. and V., post towns by a curious sign ↑, which was in vogue for a century, and, to quote from an "Explanation," "Parliamentary Boroughs have Stars annex'd to them."

Many fine town plans were published during this period, especially after 1700, but that of London, surveyed by Ogilby, his partner, William Morgan, and others and published by Morgan in 1682, is probably the most impressive ever engraved in England. The scale is an inch to 300 feet, and together with a mass of other information it includes a most interesting list of all the streets, lanes, hospitals, inns, taverns, yards, courts, alleys and rents in London and Westminster.

John Rocque, a French surveyor and engraver who came to England about 1734, introduced a style all his own in map-making. Until about 1750 he was employed in making plans of the stately new mansions and parks belonging to noblemen and merchants which Evelyn and Defoe describe so frequently. During that work he seems to have acquired a habit of engraving cultivated land, gardens, pasture, heath and the like in a realistic way, as seen in plan. At any rate his maps of Shropshire, Middlesex, Berkshire and Surrey (1752-68) show a multitude of details found previously only upon MS. estate plans, which are as delightful to the eye as they are instructive in physiography and contemporary land-utilization. He set a new standard in cartography by always depicting hills in plan. They are vertically shaded, that is, the light is supposed to fall upon them from directly above, so that the summits are white and the slopes shaded all round. Though not yet hachures, the lines of shading are thickest where the slopes are steep. In 1746 he published a famous plan of London on a scale of 5″ to the mile and accompanied by a list of streets, inns, closes, *etc.*, even more fascinating than Morgan's, and in the same year, *London and the Country Ten Miles Round*, which it is a joy to peruse. Except for two of Cornwall, Rocque's county maps were the first on a large scale.

MS. estate plans were, like their period, large but heavy in style. The writing hand of the time was also pompous, and some estate plans bear fine exhibitions of the penman's art, for in the provinces surveyors

32

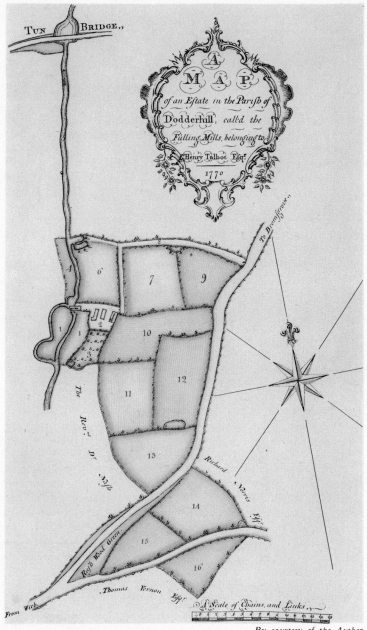

THE ESTATE OF CHARLES HENRY TALBOT, DODDERHILL, 1770
Typical MS. Estate Map of the Eighteenth Century

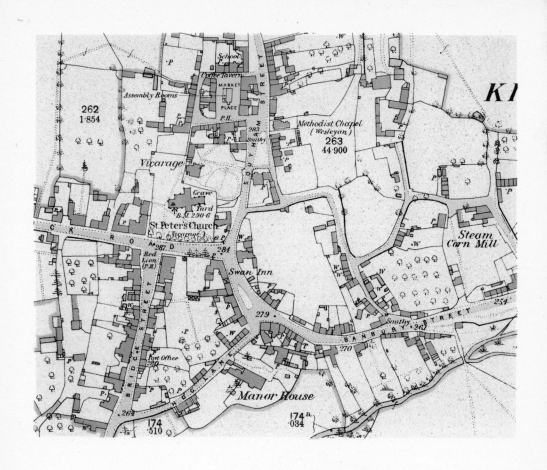

THE VILLAGE OF KINETON, WARWICKSHIRE
From the 25-in. Ordnance Survey Map, 1st edition, 1885-1887
By courtesy of the Director-General, Ordnance Survey

were usually also teachers of writing and of mathematics. One of their chief tasks was surveying for enclosure awards. From 1660 onwards parish common lands were steadily enclosed, usually by private Acts of Parliament passed after agreement among the inhabitants of the parish. Although waste lands were often awarded to the lord of the manor, these enclosures generally benefitted the farmer and smallholder.

The style of decoration on cartouches between 1660 and 1700 was baroque, often coloured but poorly engraved. Intricate plastic volutes, adorned with heavy designs of flowers and fruit, plump cherubs and floating ribbons were mingled with insipid rustic scenes and Neptunes surrounded by splashing nereids. The Late Renascence style in interior decoration, with its immense ceiling paintings of classical subjects by Verrio and Thornhill began to influence maps after 1710. Thus Queen Anne and the first two Georges are often portrayed reclining upon clouds, dressed in buskins, wreaths and flimsy robes and twanging lyres, while the noble but submissive natives of the country represented offer them homage and gifts. The decoration in Bowen & Kitchin's *Large English Atlas* is typical of its time, picturesque groups of country folk carrying on the occupation or industry peculiar to their county.

After the Civil War, the greater part of Ireland was confiscated by Cromwell, and the lands earmarked for "the adventurers for lands in Ireland, the arrears due to the souldiery there and of the publique debt." For this purpose Sir William Petty carried out a survey which was the most comprehensive and scientific survey of a large area made by any Englishman before 1755. The provincial and county maps in his atlas, *Hiberniae Delineatio* (1685), remained the standard for a century, being widely copied ; but he did not publish his large-scale maps of 214 baronies because French corsairs captured them while they were on their way to London. In 1752 John Noble and James Keenan surveyed and published a good map of county Kildare on a scale of 1″ to a mile ; this being the first map of its kind produced by Irishmen. Rocque went to Ireland about 1754, and soon published fine plans of Dublin and Cork and maps of counties Dublin and Armagh. The latter owe much to Petty's survey, but are larger and much more artistic.

In Scotland, Timothy Pont, a minister, who was inspired by the example of his contemporary, Saxton, travelled over much of the country between 1595 and 1608 making topographical drawings ; but he knew nothing of surveying, and his MSS. were neglected after his death. About 1639 Robert Gordon of Straloch began the labour of constructing readable maps from them, while Sir John Scott of Scotstarvet undertook to raise money and have the atlas published by Joan Blaeu, the only possible engraver at the time. It was published in Part V of Blaeu's *Atlas Major* in 1654. After 1678 Scotland was mapped fairly thoroughly, though piecemeal, by a number of men. The Union with England in 1707

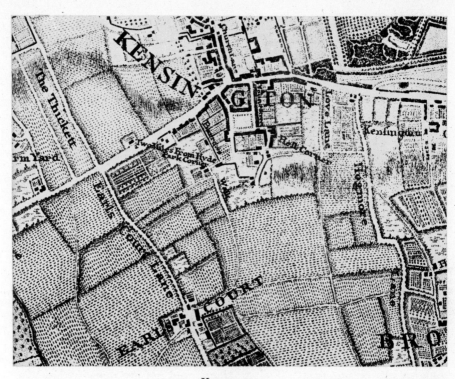

KENSINGTON
From J. Rocque's *London and the Country Ten Miles Round*, 1746

brought Scotland into the market for English publishers, and on Moll's large map, *The North Part of Britain called Scotland* (1714) the outline of the country was greatly improved. After the '15 rebellion the government had to bestir itself, and in 1725 General Wade began his famous military roads southwards from Inverness. After the '45, however, the dread inspired by clansmen was so great that in 1747 Colonel Watson was ordered to begin a detailed military survey of the Highlands on a scale of 1″=1,000 yards, which later included part of the Lowlands. It was completed in 1755, having been mainly carried out by William Roy, who began as Watson's clerk but ended as his deputy and later became one of the founders of the Ordnance Survey. The maps, which cover 84 rolls and 38 sections, are among our national treasures in the British Museum. Meanwhile John Laurie's map of the Lothians, published in 1745, was the first British map on which the altitudes of hills—very necessary in Scotland—were given. They were in feet above sea-level, but without any datum line, and vertical shading was used to portray the slopes.

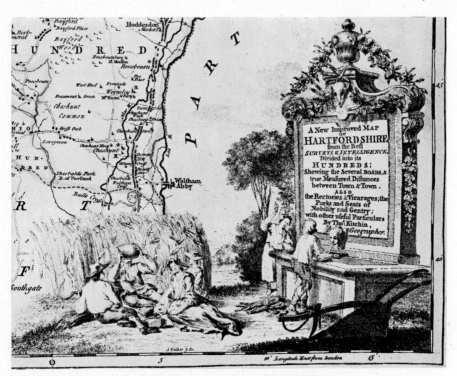

DETAIL FROM A MAP OF HERTFORDSHIRE
From Bowen and Kitchin's *Large* English *Atlas*, c. 1754

With the capture of Jamaica from Spain (1655) and of New Amsterdam (New York) from the Dutch (1664), and the foundation of Carolina (1663), Pennsylvania and New Jersey (1682) and Georgia (1732), maps by colonist surveyors multiplied rapidly. Mayo shows Barbados, which was always the political centre of the West Indies, as covered with sugar refineries. The cartouche of this map is mainly in the style of 1680, with pseudo-classical figures added. From 1660 onwards the sea came into the daily life of the English people as never before, and the naval contest with the Dutch and the growth of sea-trade—England's exports increased four-fold between 1660 and 1700—created an urgent demand for charts. About 1670, John Seller, having obtained the title of Hydrographer to the King, began the publication of volumes of charts of the northern coasts of Europe entitled *The English Pilot* and *The Coasting Pilot*. Of most of these, however, Pepys remarked "he had bought the old worn Dutch copper plates for old copper and had refreshed them in many places," a fact obvious on inspection, though Seller obtained

35

a few original charts from Englishmen like Sir Jonas Moore. Perhaps in consequence of this, Charles II commissioned Captain Greenvile Collins in 1676 to chart the coasts of Great Britain. The result, his *Great Britain's Coasting Pilot*, 1693, was the first original engraved sea-atlas by an Englishman, after Dudley's *Arcano*, and covered the whole English coast, part of the east coast of Scotland and selected Irish harbours. The charts were finely engraved, and though they seldom gave latitudes and never longitudes, showed coast features, soundings, shoals, anchorages and rocks—denoted by x—in detail, with numerous bearing-lines from points out at sea to prominent landmarks.

Many obscure local pilots began to show remarkable knowledge and skill in charting after about 1730. Outstanding is a chart of the coast between Furness and Anglesea published by Sam. Fearon and John Eyles of Liverpool in 1738, which is almost modern in its style. It is the first known chart with the prime meridian drawn through Greenwich. The sea-bottom—mud, gravel, shells, red mud, etc.—is described as on modern charts ; arrows indicate the set of the tides, and Roman letters in different places the time of High Water at full and change of the moon. Beacons and buoys are shown ; legends over dangerous rocks and shoals indicate their depth at different states of the tide ; the magnetic declination is given ; and there is no lack of useful silhouettes.

Such few ocean charts as Englishmen made were generally drawn, not upon Wright's projection, but were "plain charts" with equidistant parallels. After 1700 longitude was reckoned West as well as East. Early in the century the English began to use French instead of Dutch charts for long voyages, for the French had become the world's leading navigators. The credit of first throwing open the Pacific Ocean to the world belongs, however, to English buccaneers and many charts of the unknown Pacific were brought home by them between 1683 and 1691. At Wapping, Captain William Hack, probably a retired buccaneer, made beautiful MS. coloured copies of these. They were sold in sumptuous volumes called "South Sea Waggoners," and Lamb's words "Dusty maps of Mexico, dim as dreams, and soundings of the Bay of Panama" were inspired by one of these, preserved in the South Sea Company's House.

In 1688 Edmund Halley, Newton's friend, published a meteorological chart of the trade winds, which was invaluable to the merchantmen of the East India Company ; but his two charts showing the magnetic declination over the Atlantic (1701) and over the whole world (1702), for the year 1700, were of incalculable benefit to all navigators, only to be compared with the introduction of the compass.

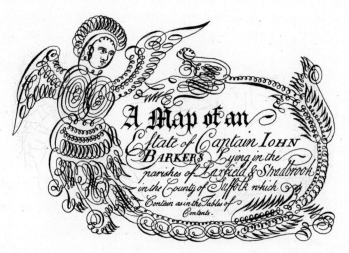

THE AGE OF REASON, ROMANTICISM and ROCOCO
1760-1800

During the age which produced Pitt and Washington, Cook and James Watt, map-making in England made prodigious advances. In 1759 the newly-formed Society of Arts offered an annual reward for an accurate survey of any English county on a scale of 1″ to 1 mile. The first map to win this was Devonshire (1765) by Benjamin Donn, a teacher of mathematics at Bideford. It was a plainer map than any before it, but more scientific, and covered twelve sheets. Inset were large and valuable plans of Exeter and Plymouth. It was engraved by Thomas Jefferys, who was also an expert surveyor and a map publisher. In 1752, indeed, he had issued the last known edition of Saxton's atlas from the scratched and battered old plates. He became Geographer to the King, and from 1766 onwards he surveyed, engraved and published several county maps which set a new standard in cartography. Though similar to Donn's Devonshire, they are distinguished by the use of the meridian of Greenwich.

Between 1765 and 1808 thirteen county maps received awards from the Royal Society of Arts, and over thirty others, of equal or greater merit, were brought out by other men, previously unknown, whose work reveals the proficiency attained by surveyors by 1790. Many of them were also their own engravers. These county maps were the most beautiful since Saxton's, and of course much superior cartographically. They had many common features. Since their scale was one, often two, inches to the mile, they covered several sheets, which generally included two or more

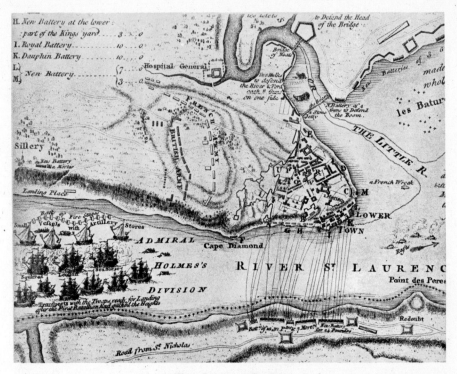

THE SIEGE OF QUEBEC
From a plan by T. Jefferys, 1759

large inset town-plans. The meridian was usually that of Greenwich, and on many there were also county meridians drawn through the capital towns. The triangulation upon which the map had been constructed was often printed for inspection. The angles were observed from hill-tops and church towers just as in Cuningham's time, but the triangulation was spherical, "reduced to a horizontal plane." Everything was shown in plan with the exception of "seats" and churches, which remained "in prospect," probably to attract subscriptions from the squire and parson, and the names of landowners were supplied in handsome Italics. Woods were depicted as compact clumps of little tree-tops, parks were often stippled in colour almost exactly as on modern Ordnance Survey maps, and distances were marked at milestones. Coasts were lapped by delicate, receding wave-lines, a convention first found on English maps in 1731. The representation of relief by vertical shading was improved—although on America, Jefferys was just then introducing "woolly caterpillar" ranges of mountains. While some publishers restricted colour to borders,

38

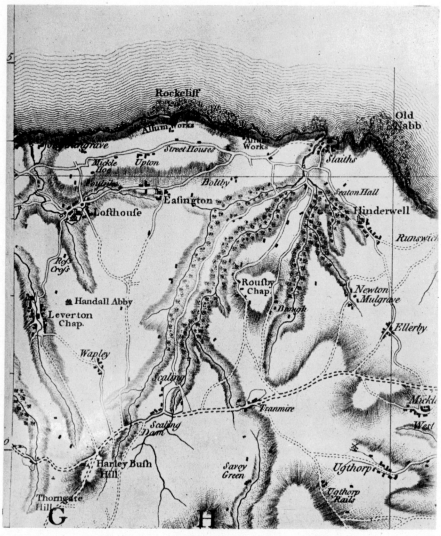

DETAIL FROM T. JEFFERYS' MAP OF YORKSHIRE, 1770

boundaries and main roads, most of these maps were coloured delightfully. They express the good taste of the age, and depict an England in which eighty per cent of the population was still rural. The colour-wash was lighter than in earlier periods, and the whole surface of each Hundred was tinted in a different hue from its neighbours. The double graduated

39

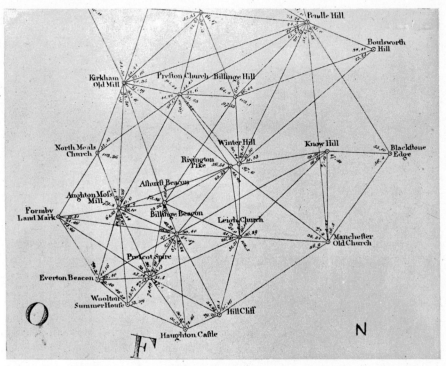

TRIANGULATION ON W. YATES'S MAP OF LANCASHIRE, 1786

lines round the maps were filled with a band of buff, and the main roads were the same colour ; towns were scarlet ("an exceeding glorious Red," wrote one colourist), water blue and woods grey-green. Italic lettering was confined to minor features, but it was graceful, and "Old Print," or Black Letter was used for Roman camps and roads. Although the "Explanation" was retained, many of the old complicated symbols were dropped. Such large maps were, however, only suitable for libraries, and in 1787 John Cary, an enterprising publisher, began to issue small county atlases, which were cheap and showed the roads at a glance. The growing seasonal influx of the gentry to fashionable Spas and sea-side resorts kept the mail-coaches busy, and Cary was engaged in 1794 by the Postmaster General to survey the main roads of the kingdom, covering some nine thousand miles. The plates in his *Survey of the High Roads from London to Hampton Court* are very pleasing, and as brightly painted as the four-in-hand coaches which the Prince of Wales drove with elegance and dash. A list of local inns heads each plate, and the lines from the roads indicate points from which handsome residences can be viewed.

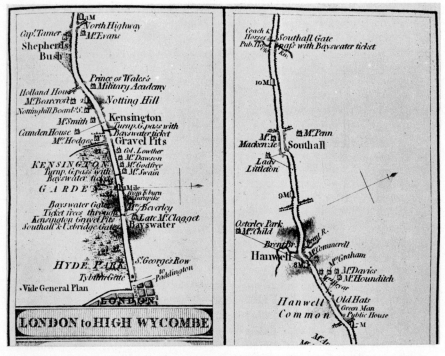

DETAIL FROM J. CARY'S *SURVEY OF THE HIGH ROADS FROM LONDON*, 1790.

The movement started by the Royal Society of Arts soon spread to Scotland. Between 1772 and 1783 John Ainslie produced a fine and accurate map of the country in nine sheets, a large plan of Edinburgh and five county maps at $1'' = 1$ mile. Andrew and Mostyn Armstrong, though their work was less reliable than Ainslie's, made four other county maps on the same scale, and Charles Ross and James Stobie carried on the work in other counties and cities. The maps were reduced and collected in Mostyn Armstrong's little *Scotch Atlas*, 1777. In Ireland the building of fine Georgian mansions all over the country was accompanied by a demand among the gentry for large-scale maps. Five county maps, two of them by Arthur Nevill, and a map of the diocese of Meath were published 1770-1797, and improved maps of Ireland were produced by Rev. D. A. Beaufort in 1792 and Lieut. A. Taylor in 1794. Beaufort had a strong ecclesiastical bent, marking every possible kind of curacy and chapel of ease, but Taylor was chiefly interested in the roads, which he showed clearly. The *Hibernian Atlas*, 1776, by Bernard Scalé, though small, contained accurate, well-engraved maps. G. Taylor and A. Skinner

41

did for Scotland and Ireland what Ogilby had done for England a century earlier when they published *A General Map of the Roads of Scotland* (1776) and *Taylor and Skinner's Maps of the Roads of Ireland* (1778). These are volumes of strip-maps, charmingly engraved and giving the names of the owners of country seats near the roads.

The manuscript maps of this period were also more handsome than any since 1610. Estate plans became very numerous, for every county landowner thought it wise to have his tenants' fields accurately surveyed, and agreeable to have his estate, often with "prospects" and artificial lakes by Capability Brown, mapped in colours. Among the best of the many good estate surveyors were Thomas Richardson, who made a glorious map of the Royal Manor of Richmond (1771) and Joshua Rhodes, who mapped most of semi-rural Kensington.

Instruction in "The Use of the Globes, Terrestial and Celestial" was part of the education of every young gentleman and gentlewoman in those days. This is something we should never have abandoned, for it can make the mysteries of geodesy, latitude and longitude, and map projections simple to any student. Neither in beauty nor usefulness can modern globes compare with those of 1790.

As England rose to naval and commercial supremacy on every ocean, charts of foreign waters by English sailors became numerous. The determination of longitude, which for centuries had been a problem for navigators, was made comparatively easy by the accurate chronometers constructed by John Harrison in 1765-71. James Cook, once a hand on a Whitby collier, first won distinction in the Navy by charting the River St. Lawrence below Quebec in preparation for General Wolfe's victorious assault in 1759. The charts which he, with Michael Lane, made of the coasts of Newfoundland in 1763-67 were so good that they were republished for years. Jefferys' *North American Pilot* and his *Western Neptune* (1776-80) reveal his great versatility, though the originals of his charts were drawn by long-forgotten pilots, such as Anthony Smith, author of a splendid chart of Chesapeake Bay.

In 1757-62 Alexander Dalrymple, a clerk under the East India Company at Madras, perceiving the great possibilities of trade in the East Indies, made several voyages thither and into the Pacific. He taught himself sea-surveying, and in 1779 the Company appointed him its first hydrographer. In 1794, when the Admiralty decided to establish a Hydrographic Office, he was made Hydrographer and is the initiator of our modern Admiralty charts.

Decoration on both charts and maps was confined to the title and dedication. The title was often set in a romantic-pastoral scene with a spreading tree and a placid river, tastefully coloured and fit to illustrate the contemporary song, "By thy banks, gentle Stour"; the dedication had a rococo frame. The light rococo style in ornament succeeded the

SUSSEX

From T. Moule's *English Counties Depicted*, 1838

late Renascence style about 1740, like a minuet following upon an oratorio, and became very popular through Chippendale's use of it in furniture. It soon appeared on maps, and was much favoured by draftsmen of estate plans. As in the last period, a stock subject was pseudo-classical female figures surrounded by products of the country represented ; but now the ladies were really attractive, resembling contemporary portraits of Duchesses as Juno, and artistically grouped. A variety of handsome copper-plate styles of writing, Italic and Roman, were combined in the title and dedication. After 1780 flourishing inscriptions, framed in a medallion such as the Adam brothers had made fashionable, were the only decorative features on many maps.

THE ORDNANCE SURVEY AND LITHOGRAPHY
1800-1935

In 1801, just two hundred years after Woutneel's first map, the publishers of English county maps encountered a competitor which eventually eclipsed them. This was the Ordnance Survey. After completing the Military Survey of Scotland, General William Roy had greatly desired to see a national survey established. His opportunity came when a partial triangulation of Kent was decided upon, so that English and French geodesists, working from Dover and Calais, could determine the difference in longitude between their national Observatories at Greenwich and Paris. For this Roy measured a base-line at Hounslow Heath in 1784. Though he died in 1790, the Duke of Richmond, Master of the Ordnance, continued the triangulation, and in 1791 formally established the Ordnance Survey, with headquarters at the Tower. Its officers, among whom a young Lieutenant, William Mudge, was the leading spirit, had orders to map Kent, Surrey, Sussex and Essex on a scale of 1″ to the mile. The instruments which they needed were supplied by Jesse Ramsden, a Yorkshireman who was then the most skilful instrument maker in the world. In 1801 the Trigonometrical Survey, as it was then called, published its first map, Kent, in four sheets ; and Essex, issued in 1805, began the series of 1″ sheets which have become as much part of our daily life as the Post Office. The Ordnance Survey is a branch of the Royal Corps of Sappers and Miners ; and its first officers had to be not only expert surveyors, mathematicians and astronomers, but hardy mountaineers.

The first task, the triangulation of Great Britain and Ireland, took over fifty years. Of many bases measured, those on Salisbury Plain (1849) and at Lough Foyle (1825) are the two principal. The largest or primary, triangles had sides of 111 to 35 miles long, the smallest had sides between 1 and 10 miles long, and within the last the chain-men began their work. The trigonometrical stations were usually on hill-tops, but church-towers,

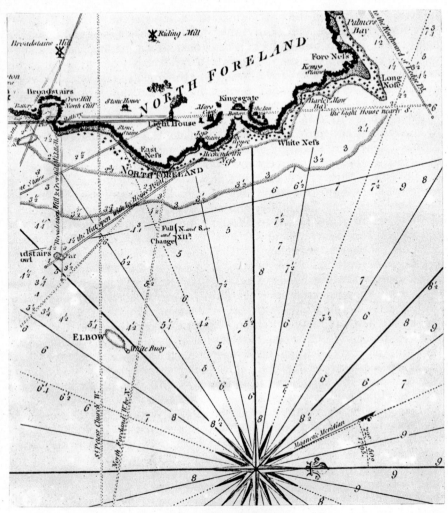

THE NORTH FORELAND
From a chart of the Downs by Trinity House Pilots, 1796

such as that at Norwich whence Cuningham had observed the angles to neighbouring churches in 1559 were often used. These points are marked on the O.S. sheets by little triangles. The levelling, that is, the determination of all heights over the whole country, from Hampstead Heath to Ben Nevis, in order that areas might be represented accurately on a horizontal plane corresponding to sea-level, took over sixty years.

The first edition of the 1″ O.S. map was completed in 1853. The sheets were uncoloured and decorously official, except for ornamental engraved handwriting in the titles, and a border of neat strokes joining the graduated double lines round the map. Parks and farmyards were stippled, sands and rivers represented by wave-lines, but gentlemen's seats were no longer distinguished by their owners' names, for the Ordnance Survey sought neither patronage nor subscriptions.

Meanwhile Jefferys' principal successors, William Faden, Aaron Arrowsmith, Cary and Thomson, had made English maps the best in Europe. They and the army of professional men who worked for them—surveyors, draftsmen, engravers and colourers—naturally looked askance at the Ordnance Survey, but their business was little affected at first. The world, which was growing larger almost every day, was still their oyster, and they published some fine atlases and new maps of distant lands, especially of those recently discovered in Western North America, the Pacific and Australia. Nor was England yet lost to them, for the first O.S. sheets came out, of course, very slowly. Two fine series of county maps at 1″ to the mile, surveyed and published by A. Bryant and C. and J. Greenwood respectively, 1820-1834, are typical of this period. Though very like the O.S. maps in most respects, including the ornamental lettering of the titles and the borders, they were better because such important details as the county, Hundred and parish boundaries were made clear in "Explanations." The early O.S. maps bore no list of symbols, nor did they copy the maps of 1770 by using Black Letter for antiquities until after 1830.

Views engraved on steel were then becoming popular for their delicate effects of light and shade, and from about 1825 to 1852 a number of maps such as Moule's Sussex were thus engraved.

Lithography, or printing from soft stone, largely took the place of engraving in the production of English commercial maps after about 1852. It was a quick, cheap process and had been used to print British army maps during the Peninsular War. Most of the commercial maps of the second half of the nineteenth century were lithographed and unattractive, though accurate enough.

The earliest maps of the Ordnance Survey on a scale of 6″ to the mile were of Ireland. The extent of the properties held by many landlords was in dispute, for the lands acquired by them in the seventeenth century had been in "plantation measure," in which the acre was 1·63 of the statute. In 1825, therefore, Parliament ordered a survey of Ireland. Thomas Colby, a man who equalled Mudge in talent and originality, was then Director-General, and by 1847 he had published a 6″ map of the whole country.

The success of this 6″ map of Ireland for the valuation of land caused a similar map of Great Britain to be begun in 1846. Sir Henry James, the Director General of the Survey, realized however that what the nation

ST. IVES BAY
From the Ordnance Survey one-inch Map, 1st Edition, 1809

and its individual citizens chiefly needed was a large-scale cadastral map that would show in detail every parcel of land in the country. For lack of such a map the railway companies and the officials employed under the Tithe Commutation Act were spending millions on maps surveyed by private engineers, and the industrial areas which were then spreading fast across the face of England called for large-scale maps. Accordingly he planned what we now know as the twenty-five inch map ; but not until 1864 did the O.S. obtain the authority, the men and the money to proceed with its full programme. This comprised the 1″ or "topographical map" revised, the 6″ or "county plans," the 25″ or "parish plans," and finally plans on a scale of 1 : 500 for every town with over four thousand inhabitants. The first edition of the 6″ was published in 1846-96, that of the 25″ in 1846-93, and all have been since revised. The five-foot plan of London was finished in 1871. In 1875 the 25″ was approved as the legal "Public Map" for the transfer of land ; in 1879 the establishment of Local Government all over the country caused the representation of the old ecclesiastical parishes, Hundreds and Wapentakes to be discontinued in favour of civil parishes ; while soon afterwards the wasteful and confusing system of publishing the 25″ sheets as parish maps was also discontinued. In Ireland and Scotland branches of the O.S. mapped those countries on the same methods and scales as England.

47

On the familiar 1″ maps engraving was continued longest. By 1853 vertical hill-shading became hachuring, a system invented to express gradients by the closeness of the shading. Though picturesque, it entailed great labour and was never very accurate. A far better method, contours or lines joining points of equal height on hill-sides, was used on the 6″ sheets from the beginning, first in black, then in blue and finally in red. The age-old custom of colouring maps by hand ceased in 1902.

In the naughty nineties the one-inch sheets suddenly appeared in a gayer and much improved dress, largely in consequence of the spread of cycling and a demand for maps which the Kippses of the time could understand. A list of conventional symbols, at first uncoloured and scantier than Norden's or Jefferys', was inserted ; hachures were tinted a pleasant brown, which did not obscure other features ; a marginal index in figures and numbers appeared ; blue wave lines and submarine contours surrounded the coasts ; roads were yellow, woods green and contours red. The Popular edition, begun after the World War, was brilliant with Elizabethan colours and had an illustrated cover which, even to the Royal Arms, was a modern version of the pictures which adorned the titles of maps in 1770. Hachuring or hill-shading was omitted, after a life of nearly two centuries. The spread of hiking brought in a symbol for Youth Hostels, and motorists made a classification of the roads necessary. These were red, yellow and plain, just as post-roads and turnpike-roads had been blue and yellow in 1835. Much more attention was paid to lettering, which became varied and artistic. There is no need to describe the splendid Fifth edition (1931), drawn on a transverse Mercator projection. It shows many features formerly found only on the large-scale plans together with very modern ones, like electric pylons ; the table of symbols has expanded and has, at last, a name, "Reference" ; and the lettering includes some delicate Italics almost worthy of Ryther. A reference grid has now replaced the marginal index, but this is likely to give place to the military grid.

The maps of the Ordnance Survey, admitted from the beginning to be the best in the world, are now also the most informative and most artistic. The Ordnance Survey has become an integral part of our national life, for there is no public body, from Rural District Councils and Sewerage Commissions to the War Office, the Land Registry and the Parliamentary Boundary Commissions, which is not deeply in its debt. It will play a great part in England's future development.